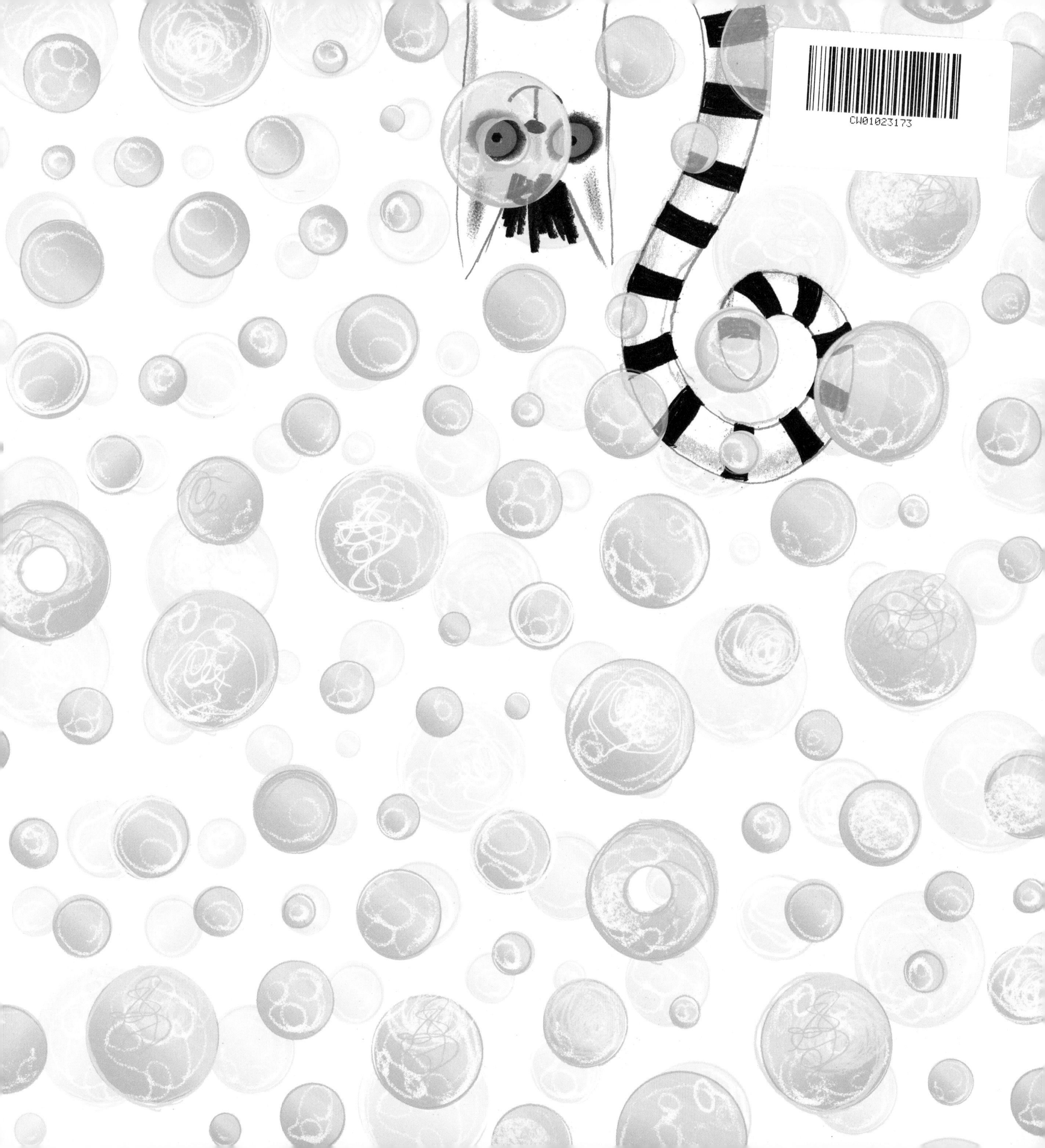

For Jasper

First published in Great Britain in 2021 by Hodder and Stoughton

Hodder Children's Books
An imprint of Hachette Children's Group
Part of Hodder and Stoughton
Carmelite House
50 Victoria Embankment
London, EC4Y 0DZ

A catalogue record of this book is available from the British Library.

HB ISBN 978 1 444 94826 4
PB ISBN 978 1 444 94827 1

1 3 5 7 9 10 8 6 4 2

Printed in China

An Hachette UK Company
www.hachette.co.uk

MIX
Paper from responsible sources
FSC® C104740

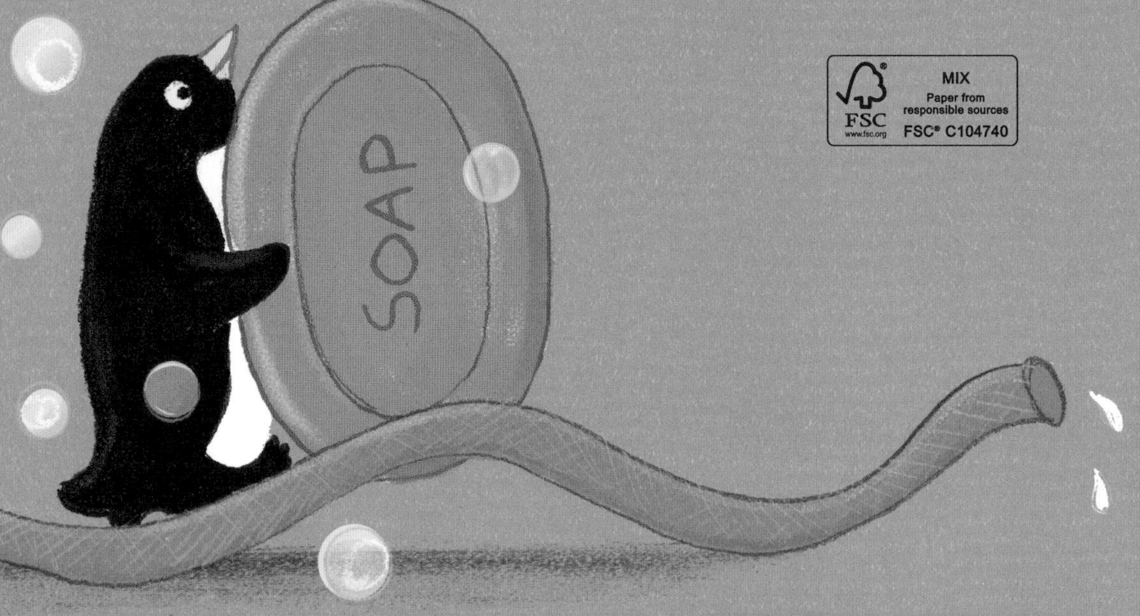

Wash Your Hands, Mr Panda

Steve Antony

Roll up, roll up, doughnuts for everyone!

PLEASE WASH
YOUR HANDS
FIRST!

Hello, Lemur. Have you washed your hands?

No, Mr Panda. But
I washed my tail!

That's good, Lemur.
But remember
to wash your
hands after
playing outside.

Have you washed your hands, Hippo?

No, Mr Panda.
But my bottom is
squeaky clean!
That's good,
Hippo. But
remember
to wash your
hands after
you've been
to the toilet.

How about you, Mice?

Oh dear! Remember to
wash your hands after
coughs and sneezes.
ACHOO!

Are your hands
clean, Bunny?

No. But
I washed
my ears.

I washed my feet.

I washed my pants.

I washed my car.
BEEP, BEEP!

Hasn't anyone washed their **HANDS?**

But why should we
wash our hands,
Mr Panda?

To wash away the germs.

Because germs
can make you sick.

How can I
wash away
germs if I
can't even
see them?

First you need soap.

Then you need water.

Then do the rub-a-dub-dub.

The rub-a-dub-dub?
Yes, like this.

That was easy!

Then rinse and
dry to finish.

So what should
you do before
eating a doughnut?

WASH YOUR HANDS, MR PANDA!

Uh-oh,
you forgot to
say please.

Doughnuts